KS3 Science

Workbook 2

Ed Walsh

Series Editor

Gareth Price

William Collins's dream of knowledge for all began with the publication of his first book in 1819. A self-educated mill worker, he not only enriched millions of lives, but also founded a flourishing publishing house. Today, staying true to this spirit, Collins books are packed with inspiration, innovation and practical expertise. They place you at the centre of a world of possibility and give you exactly what you need to explore it.

Collins. Freedom to teach.

Published by Collins
An imprint of HarperCollinsPublishers
77-85 Fulham Palace Road
Hammersmith
London
W6 8JB

Browse the complete Collins catalogue at
www.collinseducation.com

© HarperCollinsPublishers Limited 2008

10 9 8 7 6 5 4

ISBN 978-0-00-727452-9

British Library Cataloguing in Publication Data. A Catalogue record for this publication is available from the British Library.

Commissioned by Cassandra Birmingham
Project managed by Penny Fowler
Series Editor: Edmund Walsh
Internal design by Newgen Imaging
Edited by Anita Clark
Proof read by Mitch Fitton
Page layout and illustrations by Starfish Design Editorial and Project Management Ltd
Cover design by EMC Design
Production by Arjen Jansen
Printed and bound in China

Contents

Teacher support material is available at www.collinseducation.com/KS3Science

A balanced diet

1 Match these foods to the food types they contain.

Food	Food types
Fish	Carbohydrates
Milk	Fats
Chocolate	Proteins
Potatoes	Vitamins
Oranges	Minerals

2 Give **three** reasons why we need to eat food.

1 _____

2 _____

3 _____

3 The following passage provides information about diet. Use the words in the box to fill in the gaps and complete the text.

When most people use the word 'diet' they mean they are eating less to try to lose..............
In the UK, 20% of the people are 'on a diet' almost all the time! When scientists use the word
.... they mean all of the food you eat every day – whether you are trying to lose weight or
not. Doctors recommend that we should all have a .... diet. This means we eat a
.... of foods in the correct amounts to keep us................. .

| diet | healthy | balanced | weight | selection |

4 We cannot digest fibre – it passes straight through our gut. Why, therefore, do doctors recommend that we include some fibre in our diet?

_____

_____

Is my diet OK?

1 **a** List all the fruit and vegetables that you ate yesterday.

_____

_____

b Which **three** of the following do fruit and vegetables provide? Circle your answers.

proteins   vitamins   fibre   salt   minerals

2 Sort the following foods into the correct columns in the table below.

fruit   starchy vegetables   salt   fats   fish   sweets

Eat more of these	Eat less of these

3 Match the food problems to the damage they do in the body.

Diet problem	Damage in body
High fat and sugar diet	Can lead to obesity
Only eating one type of food, say chips!	Can cause an increase in blood pressure leading to heart attacks and strokes
High salt diet	Not enough vitamins to keep the body health
A diet with no fruit or vegetables	Not enough variety to give a balanced diet

4 Working in pairs, one member of the pair should:

a explain why eating breakfast can actually help you to lose weight.

The other member of the pair should:

b list the damage that too much salt does in the body.

Eating food

1   **a**   How long does it take food to pass through the human gut? Circle your answer.

> 2 hours   8 hours   12 hours   16 hours   28 hours

  b   How does fibre help food to pass through the gut?

_____

_____

2   Sort these structures into the correct order, starting with the mouth.

Mouth	1	_____
Anus	2	_____
Large intestine	3	_____
Small intestine	4	_____
Stomach	5	_____
Gullet	6	_____

3   Write a sentence to explain the word 'digestion'.

_____

_____

4   The following passage provides information about how our bodies break down food. Use the words in the box to fill in the gaps and complete the text.

Food must be .... down before it can enter the body. Breaking down foods is called .... It starts in the mouth where .... break large lumps into smaller lumps. These smaller particles are passed through the gut where .... act on them. These enzymes split large molecules up into smaller molecules. The smaller molecules then pass through the .... wall into the body.

> gut   teeth   broken   enzymes   digestion

5   Working in pairs, one member of the pair should:

  a   explain how protein is digested in the body.

The other member of the pair should:

  b   explain why molecules need to be broken down before they get into the body.

Do I have enough energy?

1 List **four** things you need energy for.

1 _____

2 _____

3 _____

4 _____

2 What unit is used to measure energy? Circle your answer.

volt   gram   joule   hertz   fat units

3 Sort these people according to who needs the most energy. Start with the person needing the least energy.

A teenage girl who plays a lot of sport   1 _____

A professional athlete training for a marathon   2 _____

A male office worker   3 _____

A pensioner in a home who cannot get around much 4 _____

A labourer building the Olympic village in London 5 _____

4 The following passage provides information about respiration. Use the words in the box to fill in the gaps and complete the text.

Respiration happens in .... cell in the body. Respiration reacts .... and oxygen to give carbon dioxide and water and release .... This energy keeps us alive. Without respiration cells die very quickly. Oxygen is taken out of the air by the .... and passed around the body in the blood. The carbon dioxide made by .... must be removed so it is passed to the lungs in the blood and breathed out.

glucose   respiration   energy   every   lungs

5 Working in pairs, one member of the pair should:

a explain why people tend to put on weight as they get older.

The other member of the pair should:

b explain the meaning of the saying: 'You don't stop exercising because you get older, you get older because you stop exercising'.

A breath of fresh air

1 Circle the correct answer. Animals take in oxygen to:

    a   use in respiration

    b   clear away carbon dioxide

    c   make sugar for energy

    d   make water

2 Write a sentence to explain the meaning of the phrase 'gas exchange'.

_____

_____

3 Label the diagram of the lungs by drawing a line from the labels to the correct part.

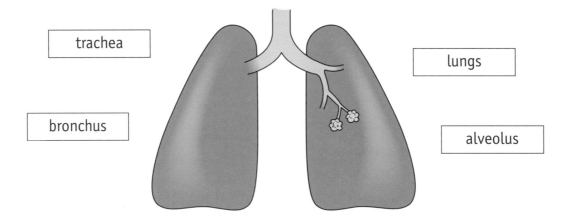

trachea

lungs

bronchus

alveolus

4 The following passage provides information about the lungs. Use the words in the box to fill in the gaps and complete the text.

The lungs produce a layer of liquid called .... that covers all the inner surfaces. .... , smoke and microbes are trapped in this liquid. Tiny hairs called cilia .... the liquid, with the trapped rubbish, over the surface of the cells towards the throat. It enters the throat and is swallowed. In the .... any dangerous organisms are destroyed. Smoking stops the cilia working properly. This is why smokers often have a bad .... – they are clearing the dirty mucus from their lungs!

cough   dust   mucus   stomach   push

5 Working in pairs, one member of the pair should:

    a explain why all animals need oxygen to survive.

The other member of the pair should:

    b describe where oxygen and carbon dioxide swap over in the lungs.

A healthy heart

1 Mark the following statements TRUE or FALSE.

    a   An artery carries blood away from the heart.

    b   A vein carries blood towards the heart.

    c   Veins have muscles to push the blood along them.

    d   A vein has a pulse.

    e   You only bleed if you cut an artery – blood cannot come out of veins.

2 Match the substance transported by the blood to its destination.

Substance	Going to...
Wastes	All cells
Oxygen	Lungs
Glucose	All cells
Carbon dioxide	Kidneys

3 The following passage provides information about oxygen and muscles. Use the words in the box to fill in the gaps and complete the text.

Athletes depend on their .... to get oxygen to their muscles at a very high rate when they are competing. Their heart rate will rise very high and their breathing rate can be .... or six times their resting rate! One way some athletes train for this is to work at very high .... for a few months before the event. Their bodies respond to the low levels of .... at high altitude by producing more red blood cells and increasing the network of vessels that supply blood to the .... .When they come back to sea level to compete they have an extra advantage.

blood   altitude   muscles   oxygen   five

4 Working in pairs, one member of the pair should:

a explain why the muscles of the heart need such a large supply of blood.

The other member of the pair should:

b explain how the heart stops blood flowing the wrong way when the muscles in the chamber walls contract.

Measuring your pulse

1 Which **three** of the following can raise your pulse rate? Circle your answers.

> exercise   smoking   drinking whisky   fear   sleeping in the cold

2 List **three** places where you can feel your pulse.

1 _____   2 _____   3 _____

3 In an experiment, a researcher looked at the pulse rate for someone before and after smoking one cigarette. The data is shown below.

Time since smoking (minutes)	Pulse rate (beats per minute)
0	63
5	90
10	85
15	78
20	69
25	65
30	60

a Draw a chart or graph to display the data.

b How long after a cigarette does it take for the pulse rate to return to normal?

_____

c A regular smoker (35 a day) and a non-smoker repeated the experiment. What difference would you expect in their pulse rate changes? Explain your answer.

_____

_____

4 Working in pairs, one member of the pair should:

a explain why a pulse can only be felt in an artery, not a vein.

The other member of the pair should:

b explain why pulse rates are different for different people even if they are all doing the same thing.

How do you know if you are fit?

1 Give **three** reasons why a marathon runner would train before an event.

1 _____

2 _____

3 _____

2 Sort the following list into the correct columns in the table below.

Low levels of exercise hardly change the pulse rate

Low levels of exercise produce a big change in pulse rate

Lungs are very large

Heart rate at rest is low

The body has a high fat level

Pulse rates take a long time to return to normal after exercise

Show someone is fit	Show someone is not very fit

3 The following passage provides information about fitness levels. Use the words in the box to fill in the gaps and complete the text.

Very fit athletes show ....changes in their pulse rate during low levels of exercise. After stopping exercise their pulse rates returns to normal very........... . Unfit people find they need longer to .... after exercise and might strain muscles during an event. This is why you should always get a health check before starting a .... programme. If you do not and you try to do too much too quickly you could damage your joints and muscles. In the worst instances you might even suffer a .... attack caused by over-straining an unfit heart.

quickly	training	recover	small	heart

4 Working in pairs, one member of the pair should:

a explain the difference between being fit and being healthy.

The other member of the pair should:

b suggest **three** ways to improve their level of fitness before a marathon run.

History of disease

1 Dr John Snow looked at the deaths from cholera in London in 1851 and 1854.

Table 1: Deaths from cholera in London 1851

District	Population in 1851	Deaths from cholera in 14 weeks ending Oct 14	Deaths per 10 000 residents
London (all districts)	2 362 236	10 367	
West	376 427	1992	
North	490 396	735	
Central	393 256	612	
East	485 522	1461	
South	616 635	5567	

  a Fill in the last column in Table 1.

  b Which district had the highest number of deaths per 100 000 people?

  c Why is it unfair to compare the total number of deaths in a district instead of the deaths per 100 000?

2 In 1854 Dr Snow concentrated on people living in South London. Different houses got water from different water companies. The figures in Table 2 are all deaths per 100 000.

Table 2: Deaths from cholera in South London 1854

Water company	Southwark and Vauxhall	Lambeth	Kent Company	Pumps	Not ascertained
Deaths from cholera	2353	302	191	279	795

  a Draw a chart to illustrate the figures in Table 2.

  b Water for the Southwark and Vauxhall company came from the Thames near the centre of London. Water for the Lambeth company came from the Thames before it reached London. How could this explain the difference between the rates of deaths for these water supply companies?

The infection cycle

1 Match each disease with the way you can catch it.

Disease	How you catch it
Malaria	Unprotected sex with an infected person or exchange of blood
Typhoid	Eating food that has gone off
AIDS	Breathing in microbes in the air
Food poisoning	From an insect bite
Flu	Drinking contaminated water

2 **a** Complete the grid, using the clues below to work out the answers.

1					I					
2					N					
3					F					
4					E					
5					C					
6					T					
7					I					
8					O					
9					N					

CLUES

1. Our .... system protects us from diseases. (6 letters)
2. Poisons released by microbes. (6 letters)
3. The short name for influenza. (3 letters)
4. An over-reaction by our immune system. (7 letters)
5. Microbes need to .... in the body before symptoms appear. (8 letters)
6. The signs that show a disease is present. (8 letters)
7. Another name for illness. (7 letters)
8. A disease-causing organism. (8 letters)
9. Something caused by a microbe. (7 letters)

b Now write your own clue for the word 'infection'.

_____

_____

3 Working in pairs, one member of the pair should:

a explain what the incubation period is.

The other member of the pair should:

b explain why people can still pass on a disease even if they show no symptoms.

Preventing disease

1 Mark the following statements TRUE or FALSE.

a Skin acts as a barrier to microbes entering the body.
b Washing hands makes infection more likely.
c Our tears contain a chemical that can destroy some microbes.
d An open wound is an easy way for microbes to get into the body.
e Tanned skin is better protection against microbes than pale skin.

2 Sort these events into the correct order. Start with the event that happens first: you cut your finger with a dirty knife.

Cut finger with dirty knife	1 _____
Skin repairs itself and scab falls off	2 _____
Scab forms to seal off cut	3 _____
Bacteria multiply in body	4 _____
Bacteria enter cut	5 _____
Antibodies produced to destroy bacteria	6 _____

3 A researcher looked at the growth of bacteria under a sticking plaster. She compared three types. The table below shows her results.

	Superstrip	Wonderplaster	Silverstick
Is the plaster waterproof?	Yes	Yes	No
Does it have antiseptic?	No	No	Yes
Bacterial growth per square cm	150	110	67

a Give **two** differences between Superstrip and Silverstick plasters.

1 _____

2 _____

b Draw a suitable graph or chart to show the different bacterial growth numbers for the sticking plasters.

c The researcher claimed that the antiseptic reduced growth of bacteria. From the table, suggest another possible explanation.

4 Working in pairs, one member of the pair should:

a explain why forming a scab at a cut is so important to the body.

The other member of the pair should:

b explain the difference between antibodies and antitoxins.

Sexually transmitted diseases

1 Which **one** of the following is not a sexually transmitted disease? Circle your answer.

| syphilis | thrush | chlamydia | smallpox | gonorrhoea |

2 Match the disease with the organism that causes it.

Disease	Organism that causes it
AIDS	Bacteria
Gonorrhoea	Bacteria
Syphilis	Fungus
Genital herpes	Virus
Thrush	Virus

3 The following passage provides information about chlamydia. Use the words in the box to fill in the gaps and complete the text.

.... is an increasing problem in the UK. It is caused by a .... and is spread by sexual activity. Unfortunately the infection often produces no .... so the sufferer does not seek treatment. The long term effects can be devastating though. Chlamydia infection can lead to .... in women. Using a .... can help to reduce the chance of catching chlamydia.

| bacterium | condom | Chlamydia | infertility | symptoms |

4 Working in pairs, one member of the pair should:

a explain the difference between HIV and AIDS.

The other member of the pair should:

b explain how people can become infected with HIV.

Biological warfare

1 Which **two** of the following do NOT spread diseases? Circle your answers.

    a   Bacteria and viruses

    b   Arrows dipped in animal dung

    c   Fungi

    d   The smell of dead bodies

    e   Changes in the phases of the Moon

2 **a**   Write a sentence to explain the meaning of the word 'quarantine'.

_____

_____

   b   When might quarantine be important?

_____

_____

3 The following passage provides information about anthrax. Use the words in the box to fill in the gaps and complete the text.

.... is a serious disease caused by a virus It kills humans very quickly and can be spread easily by tiny .... that are breathed in with the air. Military planners have tested ways to produce large .... of the anthrax spores and spray these into the air over opposing armies or towns. One problem with this technique is that even after the enemy has been .... the invading army cannot enter the area because of the anthrax ....

| Anthrax | contamination | stocks | spores | killed |

4 Working in pairs, one member of the pair should:

   a   explain how an outbreak of a dangerous disease might be controlled.

The other member of the pair should:

   b   describe how salmonella can be added to food to cause illness.

Vaccination

1 Who first developed vaccination against smallpox in the UK? Circle your answer.

    a Isaac Newton   **d** Lord Beckontree

    b Charles Darwin   **e** Charles Snow

    c Edward Jenner

2   **a** Use the data in Table 1 to plot a graph showing deaths from smallpox from 1950 to 1980.

Table 1: Global smallpox deaths from 1950 to 1980

Year	India	World
1950	157 487	332 224
1955	41 887	87 743
1960	31 091	65 737
1965	33 402	112 703
1970	12 341	33 663
1975	1436	19 278
1980	0	4500

  b When did the number of deaths from smallpox in the world fall below 20 000?

_____

  c There are no drugs to treat smallpox. Most people who catch the illness die. Write a sentence to explain why the cases of smallpox have fallen so much.

_____

_____

       vaccination   cowpox   doctor   smallpox   experiments

3 Working in pairs, one member of the pair should:

  a explain how Jenner tested his idea that cowpox could protect against smallpox.

The other member of the pair should:

  b explain what the word 'inoculate' means.

What are vaccines?

1 Look at the data in the table and then answer the questions below.

Age	Vaccinations
4 months	Diphtheria, tetanus, whooping cough, polio, Hib, Meningitis C, Pneumococcus
12 months	Meningitis C, Hib
13 months	Measles, mumps, rubella
3–5 years (before starting school)	Diphtheria, tetanus, whooping cough, polio, measles, mumps, rubella
13–18 years (for school leavers)	Diphtheria, tetanus, polio

a When do you get your first vaccination for mumps?

_____

b What vaccinations will you get when you are five years old?

_____

c How many boosters will you have had by the age of 18?

_____

2 Sort the steps on the right into the correct order to show how the mumps vaccine protects against infection with mumps.

3 Working in pairs, one member of the pair should:

a explain what a side effect is and suggest **one** vaccine that may have a side effect.

The other member of the pair should:

b explain what factors are important for a doctor when thinking about whether or not to vaccinate a child.

vaccine created in the laboratory – this is a specially weakened strain of the virus

vaccine injected into person

person's immune system reacts to the vaccine by destroying the invading virus and creating memory cells that can quickly react when the virus reappears

live virus gets into body

memory cells in the immune system quickly recognise the virus - the body reacts to produce antibodies

antibodies destroy virus before it has a chance to establish itself

How to get rid of microbes

1 Sort these situations into the correct columns in the table below.

Destroy old microbiological cultures

Gargle with a sore throat

Wipe the skin before giving a patient an injection

Wash down a lab bench before doing any microbiological work

Wash an open cut

Clean the floor in an operating theatre

Use a disinfectant	Use an antiseptic

2 An agar plate was inoculated with bacteria so that there was an even covering across the whole dish. Holes were cut in the agar and a small amount of chemical added to each one. The plate was incubated for 48 hours at 25 °C. Bacteria had died in areas around the four holes as shown in the diagram.

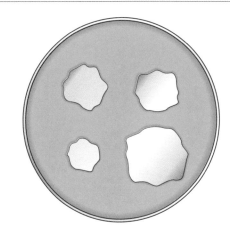

a Which chemical seemed best at killing bacteria?

_____

b What does the word 'incubate' mean? Why were the plates incubated?

_____

_____

3 Working in pairs, one member of the pair should:

a explain why washing your hands with an antiseptic gel is a good way to prevent infections being spread from ward to ward in a hospital.

The other member of the pair should:

b explain why surgeons never use their ordinary clothes when performing an operation.

Are microbes useful?

1 Sort these foods and drinks into the correct columns in the table below.

> cheese   yoghurt   chocolate   coffee   ice cream   pancakes   bread   beer

Made by microbes	No microbes needed

2 **a** Sort the steps below into the correct order to show how yoghurt is made.

Milk cooled to 45 °C in a covered container   1 _____

Your yoghurt is ready!   2 _____

Mixture of milk and bacteria left overnight in a warm place   3 _____

Milk heated to boiling to kill all microbes in it   4 _____

Special bacteria added to the cooled milk   5 _____

b Why is the milk heated to boiling first?

_____

c Why is the milk and bacteria mixture left in a warm place?

_____

d Once the yoghurt has been made it is kept in a fridge. Why?

_____

3 The following passage provides information about yeast and bread making. Use the words in the box to fill in the gaps and complete the text.

As with most microbes, ... grows more quickly in warmer conditions. Cooks know this and keep ....warm while it is rising. The rising is caused by yeast in the mixture producing carbon .... gas as it grows. The little bubbles of gas give the bread its light texture. During cooking the bread .... rises so .... that the yeast is killed. That is why bread does not continue to rise after it has been cooked!

> yeast   high   dioxide   dough   temperature

4 Working in pairs, one member of the pair should: The other member of the pair should:

a explain why, even though many microbes produce diseases, a world without microbes would not be good.

b explain why uncooked bread dough can be kept in the fridge for a few days and then taken out to rise before cooking without any problem

Topic checklist

1 Keeping healthy

Level 3

Level 4

2 Studying disease

Level 3

Level 4

Topic quiz

1 Keeping healthy

1 Suggest **two** foods rich in the following food types:
   a carbohydrates b protein c fats.
2 Give **two** pieces of advice you would offer someone in the UK who wanted to eat a healthier diet.
3 What are the **two** problems with a high salt and fat diet?
4 What unit is used to measure the energy in food?
5 a Which gas do the lungs take out of the air we breathe in?
   b Which gas do the lungs add to the air we breathe out?
6 Where would you find the trachea?
7 Why does your heart rate increase when you start to exercise?
8 Give **two** places on your body where you can feel a pulse.
9 Why do very fit athletes tend to have a low resting heart rate?
10 Explain why smokers often suffer from a cough.
11 a Mark the statements below TRUE or FALSE.
   b Rewrite the false statements to make them correct.
   • Fresh fruit and vegetables are a good source of vitamins.
   • If you take in more energy in your food than you use up you will get fat.
   • Small hair-like cells in the lung push mucus and dust towards the throat so that they can be swallowed.
   • The heart is made of muscle.
   • Office workers need less food than manual labourers to stay healthy.
   • Eating only beef burgers and drinking only fizzy drinks is an excellent, healthy diet.
   • Arteries take blood towards the heart, veins take blood away from the heart.
   • Cigarette smoking lowers your pulse rate.
   • To have a balanced diet you only really need to worry about the amount of protein you eat.

2 Studying disease

1 Suggest **three** things that can cause disease.
2 a What disease did Dr. John Snow study in London in the nineteenth century?
   b What spread this disease?
   c How did Snow prove this?
3 What system in the body protects us from disease?
4 Suggest **three** things to do to avoid catching an infection.
5 What is a sexually transmitted disease?
6 a What is a vaccine?
   b How can it protect against infection?
7 What is the difference between an antiseptic and a disinfectant?
8 List **three** foods made by microbes.
9 Why do doctors wash their hands when moving from patient to patient?
10 What disease is caused by the Human Immunodeficiency Virus (HIV)?
11 a Mark the statements below TRUE or FALSE.
   b Rewrite the false statements to make them correct.
   • Flies lay eggs in rotting meat. These hatch to form maggots. The meat does not produce the maggots itself.
   • An antibody is a chemical made by the body when a microbe enters it.
   • Smallpox has been eradicated from the Earth using vaccination to protect people.
   • Boiling kills all microbes.
   • Milk is boiled to kill off bacteria already present and then cooled before adding the yoghurt culture.
   • Microbes are not needed to produce beer.
   • The best time to vaccinate someone against polio is when they have the disease.
   • Taking certain herbs can protect you against infection with HIV.
   • Toxins are harmless chemicals produced in the body by microbes.
   • Your zodiac sign controls what sorts of diseases you will suffer from in your life.

Dissolving rocks

1 **a** Water is an excellent solvent. What does the word 'solvent' mean?

_____

b Sort these substances into the correct columns in the table below.

sugar   tea leaves   table salt   carbon   diamond   steel   paper

Dissolve in water	Do not dissolve in water

2 Circle the correct answer. Water can separate a mixture of sand and salt because:

    a sand sinks but salt floats

    b sand dissolves in water but salt does not

    c salt dissolves in water but sand does not

    d salt sinks but sand floats

    e sand and salt react together when they are dry

3 The following passage provides information about dissolving rocks. Use the words in the box to fill in the gaps and complete the text.

When water seeps through .... very small amounts of the rock .... As the water drips from the roof of a cave a tiny amount of the water evaporates. This makes the dissolved mineral, called calcium ...., come out of solution. The calcium carbonate sticks to the roof of the cave. Over hundreds of years these specks grow to form a .... When the drop of water hits the cave floor the same thing happens. But here the small particles of calcium carbonate grow into a ....

carbonate   limestone   stalagmite   stalactite   dissolve

4 Working in pairs, one member of the pair should:

a explain how a stream in a limestone-rich area can petrify an object left in the stream.

The other member of the pair should:

b explain why stalactites take so long to grow.

Sweet tooth

1 Give **two** ways you know that sugar is present in water even if you cannot see it.

1 _____

2 _____

2 Circle the correct answer. A cook will heat water before trying to dissolve sugar in it. This is because:

    a   cooks like to use cookers to heat things up

    b   sugar tastes bitter if you dissolve it in cold water

    c   sugar goes brown in cold water

    d   for health and safety reasons

    e   hot water dissolves sugar more quickly than cold water

3 If you dissolve 20 g of sugar in 100 g of water, what will the solution weigh? Circle your answer.

    80 g   90 g   100 g   110 g   120 g

4 In an experiment to investigate how temperature affects the solubility of salt in water, a student got the following results.

Temperature in °C	10	20	30	40	50	60	70	80	90
Mass of salt dissolved in g	10	16	22	28		40	56	52	58

    a Draw a graph to display these results.

    b Suggest a value for the missing result for 50 °C.

    c If you used half the amount of water, how much salt would dissolve at 20 °C?

    _____

    d One of the results looks a bit strange. Which one? Give a reason for your choice.

    _____

5 Working in pairs, one member of the pair should:

    a explain why clothes are cleaner if they are washed in hot water rather than cold mixture.

The other member of the pair should:

    b explain why the colours in some clothes fade if they are washed in hot water.

Pure salt

1 Write a sentence to explain each of the following words:

a Solution: _____

b Solute: _____

2 Rock salt is salt that has been mined from the ground. It is often not white in colour like table salt. This is because:

a rock salt contains impurities which give it a colour

b rock salt is not the same chemical as table salt

c table salt is treated with chemicals to make it white

d rock salt comes from hot countries where the colour protects it from the sunlight

e table salt is painted white during manufacturing

3 **a** Sort the following steps into the correct order for collecting salt from seawater.

The salt crystallises out of solution   1 _____

Let the sunlight evaporate the water   2 _____

Trap seawater in large, flat dishes or puddles   3 _____

Collect the salt from the dried-up pool or dish 4 _____

b Collecting salt from seawater usually only happens in countries with lots of sunshine. Explain why.

_____

_____

4 The following passage provides information about salt. Use the words in the box to fill in the gaps and complete the text.

Salt is a common ...., but it is often mixed with other................ . If we want to use salt in cooking it has to be .... to remove bits of grit or any substances that might taste bad or be dangerous. The easiest way to do this is to .... the salt in the rock salt in water and collect the salty water. This can be heated and the pure salt is left behind when all the water has

....

mineral   purified   evaporated   dissolve   substances

5 Working in pairs, one member of the pair should:

a explain why pools used to evaporate water should be wide and flat.

The other member of the pair should:

b explain why salt has to be purified before it can be used in cooking.

Super solvents

1 Circle the correct answer. Graffiti artists do not use water-soluble paints as these:

    a do not have the right colours   **d** would wash away in the rain

    b are poisonous   **e** have a bad smell

    c are very expensive

2 Write a sentence to explain the word 'insoluble'.

_____

_____

3 Mark the following statements TRUE or FALSE.

    a Water can dissolve sugar.

    b Water can dissolve grease and oil.

    c Alcohol can dissolve ballpoint pen ink.

    d Oil paints can dissolve in water.

    e White spirit can dissolve paint on a dirty paintbrush.

4 Complete this table by putting a tick in each cell if the solvent would dissolve the substance. Put a cross if it would not dissolve it. Some have been done for you as examples.

Solvent	Water	Alcohol	Acetone	White spirit
Sugar		✓		✗
Nail polish	✗			
Dried gloss paint		✗		
Oils		✓		
Scent from flowers			✓	
Road tar	✗			

5 Working in pairs, one member of the pair should:

    a explain why some solvents cannot be used near flames.

The other member of the pair should:

    b explain why you should test a solvent on a small portion of a T-shirt before you use it to remove a stain on the front.

Distillation

1 Add the correct labels to the diagram below.

Vapour
Liquid
Solid
Cooling

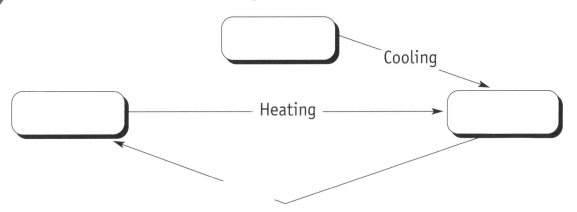

Cooling

Heating

2 Write a sentence to explain the word 'distillation'.

_____

_____

3 The diagram to the right shows a solar still. It can turn dirty water into drinking water in emergency situations such as having no available water in a desert. Study the diagram and then answer the questions below.

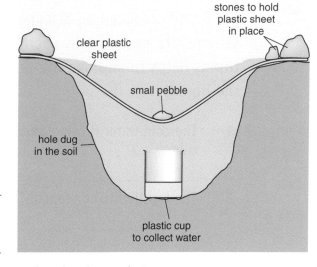

stones to hold plastic sheet in place

clear plastic sheet

small pebble

hole dug in the soil

plastic cup to collect water

a Where does the water come from?

_____

b Where does the clean water collect?

_____

c What does the stone in the middle of the clear plastic sheet do?

_____

d Where does the heat to evaporate the water come from?

_____

4 Working in pairs, one member of the pair should:

a explain why some alcoholic drinks are distilled.

The other member of the pair should:

b explain why you should use distilled water when making up solutions in a chemistry laboratory.

Better boiling

1 Suggest **two** reasons why a chemist might want to boil something in a laboratory.

1 _____

2 _____

2 Mark the following statements TRUE or FALSE.

a Packing ice around a container helps vapours to condense inside it.

b Heating a liquid increases the rate of evaporation.

c Cooling a liquid has no effect on its evaporation.

d Water only evaporates at 100 °C.

3 **a** A Liebig condenser is a device to increase the liquid produced by distillation. Write a sentence to explain how each of these things helps to improve the production of the liquid.

1 The cold water flowing around the central tube

_____

2 The tightly fitting stopper in the flask

_____

3 The down-turned delivery pipe

_____

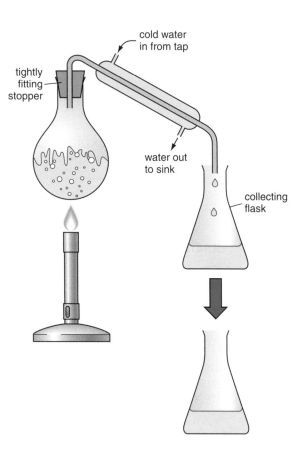

cold water in from tap

tightly fitting stopper

water out to sink

collecting flask

b Why would it not be safe to have a tightly fitting stopper in the collecting flask?

_____

c What would happen to the rate of condensation if the water in the jacket was hot instead of cold?

_____

4 Working in pairs, one member of the pair should:

a explain why some stills for making whisky have long coiled delivery tubes instead of short, straight ones.

The other member of the pair should:

b explain why many old stills are made from copper metal.

Drinking water

1 The following diagram shows the label from a bottle of mineral water.

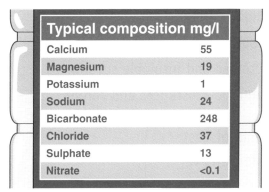

Typical composition mg/l	
Calcium	55
Magnesium	19
Potassium	1
Sodium	24
Bicarbonate	248
Chloride	37
Sulphate	13
Nitrate	<0.1

a What does the symbol 'mg' mean? Circle your answer.

milligrams   micrograms   megagrams   multigrain

b What would be the value for sodium in distilled water?

_____

c Why do some people say it is best to drink only bottled water when travelling in countries with poor water supplies?

_____

_____

2 Write a sentence to explain the meaning of the word 'desalination'.

_____

_____

3 Label these parts on a typical desalination plant.

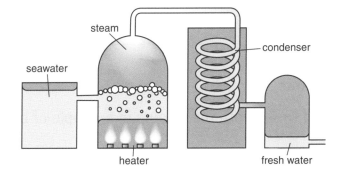

steam

condenser

seawater

heater   fresh water

4 Working in pairs, one member of the pair should:

a explain why boiled and cooled water is not the same as distilled water.

The other member of the pair should:

b explain why some desalination plants boil water under reduced pressure.

Chromatography

1 Circle the correct answer. Chromatography is used to separate:

    a   a mixture of solids

    b   a mixture of dissolved substances

    c   a mixture of dissolved and insoluble substances

    d   a mixture of magnetic substances and carbon

2 Study the chromatograms of test solutions A to E and then answer the questions below.

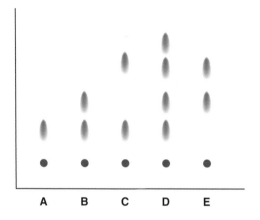

a Which one contains only one substance? ....

b Which solution contains the most substances? ....

c Two substances are actually the same. Which are these? ....

d The diagram below shows the chromatogram of the pure substance X.

    Which of the test chromatograms also contain the substance X? ....

e On the diagram, mark:

    i   the direction the solvent is moving

    ii   the slowest-moving substance in the test

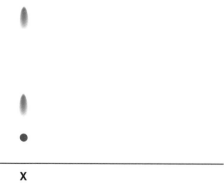

3 Working in pairs, one member of the pair should:

    a explain how chromatography can be used to separate the colours in a sample of black ink.

The other member of the pair should:

    b explain why the substances to be separated must be dissolved in something for a chromatogram to work.

Chemical alphabet

1 Circle the correct answer. An element is a chemical that:

    a   melts at room temperature

    b   contains one type of atom

    c   contains carbon and only one other substance

    d   contains a metal

    e   can be separated into two different chemicals

2 Match the chemical symbol to its element.

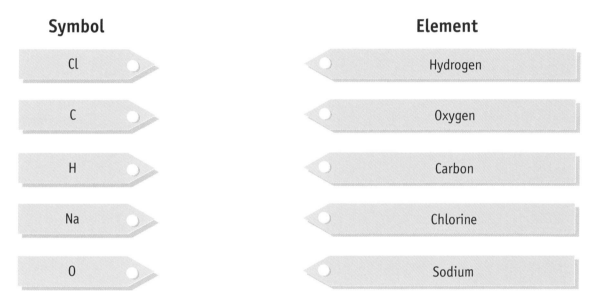

Symbol	Element
Cl	Hydrogen
C	Oxygen
H	Carbon
Na	Chlorine
O	Sodium

3 The following passage provides information about chemical symbols. Use the words in the box to fill in the gaps and complete the text.

Scientists use chemical .... to represent atoms. This helps because it is .... than using the full name for each substance. It also shows how much of .... atom is present in substances that contain more than one atom. For example, carbon dioxide is written as CO_2. This shows that there are .... as many atoms of .... as there are of carbon.

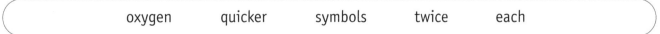

oxygen   quicker   symbols   twice   each

4 Working in pairs, one member of the pair should:

a explain why the symbols for some elements have more than one letter in them.

The other member of the pair should:

b explain which chemicals are requested by the following symbols: H, O, H_2O, CO_2, Au.

Getting sorted

1 Elements can be sorted into two groups: metals and non-metals. Sort the following characteristics into the correct columns in the table below.

Conduct electricity well

Conduct heat badly

Tend to snap when they are bent

Bend but do not break easily

Shiny, often silvery in colour

Can stretch to make wires

Describe metals	Describe non-metals

2 **a** Use the clues in the table below to sort the mystery elements into metals or non-metals. Tick the correct column for each element. One has been done as an example.

Mystery element	Solid, liquid or gas at 20 °C?	Conduct heat well?	Conduct electricity well?	Breaks when bent?	Metal?	Non-metal?
A	Solid	No	No	Yes		✓
B	Gas	No	No	Does not apply		
C	Liquid	Yes	Yes	Does not apply		
D	Liquid	No	No	Does not apply		
E	Solid	Yes	Yes	No		

b What is unusual about mystery element C?

_____

c Suggest the name of this element.

_____

3 Working in pairs, one member of the pair should:

a explain how you could tell if a mystery element was or was not a metal.

The other member of the pair should:

b explain why semi-conductors are difficult to sort into the metal or non-metal group.

All mixed up

1 Sort these substances into pure substances and mixtures.

water   pure orange juice   sugar   ice cream

honey   hydrogen   instant coffee powder

Pure substances	Mixtures

2 Mark the following statements TRUE or FALSE.

A   A mixture of two things does not have to have the same amounts of each thing all the time.

B   In a mixture the substances are chemically bonded together.

C   Mixtures are always cheaper than pure substances.

D   Mixtures can be separated by physical methods.

3 Suggest ways to separate the following mixtures:

a Specks of gold and sand

_____

b Oxygen and nitrogen in the air

_____

c Sugar and salt

_____

d Tea from tea leaves

_____

4 Working in pairs, one member of the pair should:

a explain why the chemicals in your laboratory are almost all pure substances not mixtures.

The other member of the pair should:

b explain how you know that bread and cakes are made of mixtures.

What are compounds?

1 Circle the correct answer. A compound is something formed when:

   a   two elements mix together   **d**   two or more elements join together chemically

   b   two mixtures are heated together   **e**   somebody paints a fence

   c   water turns to steam

2 Sort the following formulas into the correct columns in the table below.

H_2 H_2O C CH_4 C_2H_5OH NaCl

Elements	Compounds

3 Complete the table below showing the compounds formed when **two** elements react together.

Element 1	Element 2	Compound formed
Carbon		Carbon dioxide
Zinc	Oxygen	
	Sulphur	Iron sulphide
Iron		Iron oxide

4 The following passage provides information about compounds. Use the words in the box to fill in the gaps and complete the text.

Compounds form when two or more .... join together chemically. Compounds have completely different ....from the elements that make them up. For example, ... is a dangerous inflammable metal and chlorine is a ....gas. When they react together they make sodium .... – the same salt that you put on your chips!

   poisonous   properties   chloride   sodium   elements

5 Working in pairs, one member of the pair should:

   a   explain what are the important differences between a pile of sulphur and iron particles mixed together and a pile of iron sulphide.

The other member of the pair should:

   b   explain how you could prepare a sample of magnesium oxide.

Understanding equations

1 Complete the word equations below.

a Calcium + ... → calcium oxide
b .... + ... → sodium oxide
c .... + oxygen → water
d Sulphur + ... → sulphur dioxide
e Zinc + sulphur → ....

2 Match the symbol to the chemical it represents.

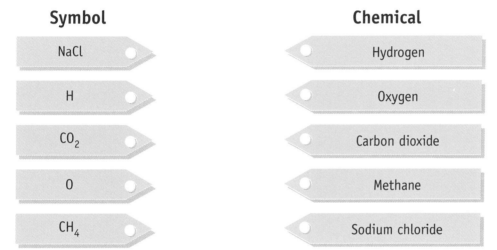

Symbol	Chemical
NaCl	Hydrogen
H	Oxygen
CO_2	Carbon dioxide
O	Methane
CH_4	Sodium chloride

3 The following passage provides information about equations. Use the words in the box to fill in the gaps and complete the text.

Chemists use .... to quickly describe what happens in a reaction. An equation using the correct ....shows which chemicals were involved in the reaction and the .... these chemicals are made from. It even shows how ....chemicals of each sort were involved! So the equation below shows that two atoms of sodium react with one oxygen atom to make a new compound, sodium .... ,with two sodium atoms to every one oxygen atom.

$$2Na + O → Na_2O$$

many	equations	elements	symbols	oxide

4 Working in pairs, one member of the pair should:

a explain how you can tell how many atoms of an element there are in a compound by looking at the formula.

The other member of the pair should:

b explain where you could find the symbols for all the elements.

Combining elements

1 Circle the correct answer. What is the ratio of males to females in the UK?

> 1:2   2:1   3:4   1:1   2:3

2 What is the ratio of oxygen to nitrogen in the compounds below?

Nitrogen-containing compounds	Oxygen:nitrogen ratio
NO_2 – a poisonous brown gas	
N_2O – laughing gas: used as an anaesthetic	
NO_3 – nitrogen trioxide: used to make nitric acid	

3 The following passage provides information about combining elements. Use the words in the box to fill in the gaps and complete the text.

Atoms do not join up .... to make compounds. They join in simple .... and any part of the compound has that same ratio. So, in a pile of pure table salt, it is the same ratio of sodium to chlorine throughout the pile. Lead can form a number of different .... All of the oxides contain just .... and oxygen but they are different because they have different ratios of lead to oxygen. This means that the atoms are .... differently in the different oxides. Therefore, they have different chemical and physical properties.

> ratios   randomly   arranged   oxides   lead

4 Working in pairs, one member of the pair should:

a explain why the ratio of different elements in a compound must be the same wherever that compound is found.

The other member of the pair should:

b explain why ratios of reacting atoms are usually simple ones.

Topic checklist

3 Separating mixtures

Level 3

Level 4

4 Atoms, elements and compounds

Level 3

Level 4

Topic quiz

3 Separating mixtures

1 a How would you separate a mixture of sand and salt?
   b Could you use the same method to separate salt and sugar? Give a reason for your answer.
2 How does the temperature of the water affect how quickly sugar dissolves?
3 Give **two** differences between rock salt and salt that you put on your chips.
4 What solvent could you use to dissolve:
   a nail varnish
   b dried gloss paint
   c road tar?
5 Why do brewers have to distil fermented liquid to make whisky?
6 a What is a Liebig condenser?
   b How does it cool the vapours coming from the boiling liquid?
7 What do some countries use desalination for?
8 What can you separate using chromatography?
9 Why do we not wash clothes in cold water even though that might be better for the environment?
10 What chemical is a stalactite made from?
11 a Mark the statements below TRUE or FALSE.
    b Rewrite the false statements to make them correct.
    • Dissolved salts in a stream in a limestone area can petrify objects left in the stream.
    • Alcohol is a useful solvent but needs to be handled carefully because it gives off vapours that catch fire easily.
    • A solar still can produce clean drinkable water from river water in an emergency.
    • Chromatography is used to check the colours in inks to detect forgeries.
    • Mineral water contains no dissolved substances at all.
    • Water-soluble means something that water can dissolve.
    • Distillation reduces the amount of alcohol in a drink.
    • The symbol mg stands for many grammes.
    • Solubility of salt goes down as the temperature is raised.

4 Atoms, elements and compounds

1 What do each of the symbols below stand for?
   a Na
   b O
   c C
   d Mg
   e Fe
2 What are the **three** states of matter?
3 Give **two** differences between metals and non-metals.
4 What does the Periodic Table list?
5 How does potassium react when it is put into water?
6 What is the difference between a pure substance and a mixture?
7 Can a compound be pure? Explain your answer.
8 What substance is made when:
   a magnesium burns in air
   b sodium burns in chlorine gas
   c lithium is added to water?
9 How many oxygen atoms are there to each carbon atom in the molecules below?
   a CO_2
   b $CaCO_3$
10 Give **one** advantage of using a symbol equation instead of a word equation.
11 a Mark the statements below TRUE or FALSE.
    b Rewrite the false statements to make them correct.
    • Metals conduct heat and electricity better than non-metals.
    • An element contains only one type of atom.
    • Elements in the same group in the Periodic Table have similar chemical properties.
    • A compound contains atoms that are joined chemically.
    • Mixtures can usually be separated by physical means.
    • Ca is the symbol for carbon.
    • All metals are solid at room temperature.
    • Carbon dioxide forms when carbon reacts with nitrogen.
    • The numbers in symbolic chemical equations are not important.
    • The formula for common table salt is $NaCl_2$.

Magnetic materials

1 Mark the following statements TRUE or FALSE.

A Iron is a magnetic material.

B Magnets can repel or attract other magnets.

C A more powerful magnet has a larger magnetic field.

D Magnetic materials are not affected by gravity.

E If you pass an electric current through a magnet it demagnetises it.

2 Where is the magnetic field around a bar magnet strongest? Circle the correct answer.

the two poles   in the middle of the magnet   at the north pole
at the south pole   it is equal across the whole magnet.

3 Explain why keeping video tapes near a powerful magnet may be a bad idea.

_____

_____

4 Use the words in the box below to fill the gaps in this passage.

The north pole of a .... should really be called the north-seeking pole. If the compass .... is allowed to turn, this pole will point towards the north. It is actually a .... pole because .... poles attract each other. The part of the needle that points south is actually a north pole! In a ....magnet it is slightly different. Here the pole that is labelled north (it is usually red in colour) is actually a north pole!

> compass   needle   south   unlike   bar

5 Working in pairs, one member of the pair should:

a list **three** things that depend on magnets to work properly.

The other member of the pair should:

b explain why a credit card should not be kept near a magnet.

Magnetic fields

1 **a** Write a sentence to explain what a magnetic field is.

_____

_____

b Explain how you could detect a magnetic field.

_____

_____

2 Look at the diagram of the magnetic flux here.

a Redraw the diagram to show a magnet with a weaker magnetic field.

b If you sprinkled iron fillings onto the magnet where would they tend to collect?

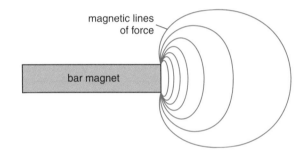

magnetic lines of force

bar magnet

3 Put a tick in the correct column in the table below.

Experiment	Objects repel each other	Objects attract each other	No effect
Two magnets are brought together with their north poles closest.			
Two magnets are brought together with their south poles closest.			
Two magnets are brought together with their north and south poles closest.			
A magnet is brought near an iron nail.			
A magnet is brought near a copper nail.			

4 Explain the difference between bringing two magnets together and bringing a magnet and a magnetic material together.

Earth's magnetic field

1 The Earth behaves like a giant bar magnet producing a magnetic field across the planet. Give **two** advantages of this effect.

1 _____

2 _____

2 Tick the correct answer from the options below. The Earth's core contains iron-rich minerals. However, we know there is not a giant permanent magnet at the core because:

A the core is too hot, iron is not magnetic above 77 °C.

B we cannot detect it using X-rays.

C the Earth is the wrong shape to contain a giant bar.

D it is a different sort of iron.

E bar magnets are made of steel not iron.

3 What is the solar wind and where does it come from?

4 Use the words in the box below to fill the gaps in this passage.

The Earth cannot contain a .... bar magnet - so what causes the magnetic............. ? Scientists now think that molten, iron-rich minerals in the .... core are constantly moving around by............... This is similar to the way that liquids move in a saucepan on a stove. These movements create the magnetic field. This idea is known as the ....theory.

> giant   field   outer   convection   geodynamic

5 Working in pairs, one member of the pair should:

a explain how the Earth's magnetic field creates the northern lights or aurora borealis.

The other member of the pair should:

b explain how the solar wind affects the shape of the Earth's magnetic field.

Explaining magnetism

1 Give **three** ways to make a permanent magnet.

1 _____

2 _____

3 _____

2 Which two of the following can be made into magnets? Circle the correct answers:

A   an iron nail

B   a steel bar

C   a strip of magnesium metal

D   a wooden ruler

E   a glass rod

3 Mark the statements below TRUE or FALSE.

A   You can magnetise an iron bar by stroking it with a permanent magnet.

B   You can demagnetise an iron bar magnet by heating it.

C   Magnets attract anything with iron in it.

D   Putting a magnet inside a solenoid carrying direct current demagnetises it.

E   All metals can be made into magnets.

4 Use the words in the box below to fill the gaps in this passage.

If you place an iron bar in a .... of wire and pass .... current through the wire, the iron bar will be magnetised. Even when the .... is switched off or the iron bar removed, the bar will still be magnetic. If you use alternating current in the coil and put a .... magnet in it, the magnetism will be destroyed. Even when the current is switched off the magnet will still be ....

| coil | direct | current | permanent | demagnetised |

5 Working in pairs, one member of the pair should:

a   explain what a magnetic domain is.

The other member of the pair should:

b   explain what happens to these magnetic domains when they are placed in a magnetic field.

Electromagnetism

1 Mark the following statements about electromagnets TRUE or FALSE

A An electromagnet is made by passing electricity through a coil of insulated wire.

B An electromagnet can be switched on and off.

C Putting a soft iron core in the coil increases the power of an electromagnet.

D All electromagnets are painted red.

E Electromagnets do not have south poles.

2 **a** Use the clues below to fill the spaces in this grid.

1						E				
2						L				
3						E				
4						C				
5						T				
6						R				
7						O				
8						M				
9						A				
10						G				
11						N				
12						E				
13						T				

1 A magnetic .... surrounds a magnet. (5 letters)
2 The loop of wire carrying the current in an electromagnet. (4 letters)
3 The flow of electricity is the .... (7 letters)
4 The .... of the flow of electricity controls which end of the electromagnet is north. (9 letters)
5 The end of the electromagnet that attracts a south pole on a permanent magnet. (5 letters)
6 A simple block of magnetised iron is sometimes called a .... magnet. (3 letters)

7 This pole of a magnet will be repelled by the south pole of an electromagnet. (5 letters)
8 A magnetised needle used to detect the direction of north. (7 letters)
9 When an electromagnet is switched on it will .... iron objects. (7 letters)
10 A magnetic field must contain .... because it can make electricity flow in a wire. (6 letters)
11 Adding more coils to an electromagnet makes it .... (8 letters)
12 Thin lengths of metal used to carry electricity in an electromagnet. (4 letters)
13 Plastic string cannot be used to make an electromagnet because it does not .... electricity. (7 letters)

b Now write a clue for the word 'electromagnet'.

3 Working in pairs, one member of the pair should:

a give **three** ways to increase the strength of an electromagnet.

The other member of the pair should:

b suggest **one** way to detect the magnetic field around an electromagnet

Using electromagnets

1 Suggest **three** uses for an electromagnet.

1 _____

2 _____

3 _____

2 Number the following steps to give the correct order to show how an electric doorbell works.
Use the diagram on the right to help you.

The hammer is pulled away from the bell.

The circuit is broken by the armature so the current stops flowing.

Electricity flows along the circuit and magnetises the coil.

The coil loses its magnetism.

Visitor presses the doorbell and completes a circuit.

The springy steel strip forces the hammer against the bell and makes a sound.

The circuit is remade so the coil becomes magnetic again and pulls the hammer away from the bell.

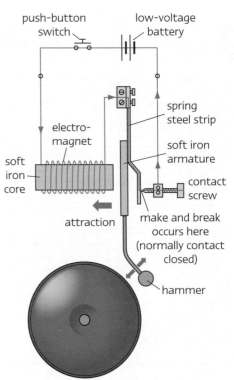

push-button switch · low-voltage battery · spring steel strip · electro-magnet · soft iron armature · soft iron core · contact screw · attraction · make and break occurs here (normally contact closed) · hammer

3 Use the words in the box below to fill the gaps in this passage.

Relays are often used to .... circuits that may carry many thousands of volts. A low-power circuit is completed when the .... presses a button. This .... a coil which flips a switch to start current in a much more .... circuit. There are two advantages to this. One is that the operator's button can be a long way from the actual switch so all of the switches in a large factory can be controlled from a single control room. The second is that people do not need to go near .... carrying very large voltages.

> control   operator   magnetises   powerful   circuits

4 Working in pairs, one member of the pair should:

a explain how a circuit breaker can protect a circuit from large surges of power.

The other member of the pair should:

b suggest **one** major advantage of a circuit breaker over a fuse which melts to break the circuit when too much current flows.

Motors and generators

1 What happens to a wire carrying a current in a magnetic field? Tick the correct answer below.

A It moves.

B It glows red hot.

C It resists the flow of electricity.

D The current starts to flow in the opposite direction.

E No change.

2 The average house contains over 20 electric motors! Suggest **three** devices that might contain an electric motor.

1 _____

2 _____

3 _____

3 Suggest **three** ways to increase the magnetic field in a coil.

1 _____

2 _____

3 _____

4 Use the words in the box below to fill the gaps in this passage.

A .... is a device that converts .... into electricity. A wire is moved in a magnetic field and this creates a current in the wire. The current passes out of the generator and can be used to power devices or charge a .... To .... the power output from a generator you can move the wire more quickly, increase the strength of the magnetic field or increase the length of the wire. Most generators have .... of wire so that you can pack a long wire into a small space.

| generator | movement | battery | increase | coils |

5 Working in pairs, one member of the pair should:

a explain why the most powerful electric motors contain very strong magnets.

The other member of the pair should:

b explain how you could speed up or slow down an electric motor.

Power stations

1 Sort these things into the correct order to show how a coal-fired power station makes electricity.

Generators produce electricity	1	_____
Coal delivered to power station	2	_____
Steam turns giant turbines	3	_____
Coal is burnt to boil water	4	_____
Turbines turn generators	5	_____

2 **a** Which **one** of the following has never been burnt in power stations to heat water? Circle your answer.

> gas   coal   oil   clay   wood

b Which **one** of the list above is a renewable resource?

_____

3 **a** Give **two** ways in which energy is wasted at a power station.

1 _____

2 _____

b Give **three** environmental problems with large power stations.

1 _____

2 _____

3 _____

4 Working in pairs, one member of the pair should:

a explain why we still use power stations even if they are inefficient and environmentally unfriendly.

The other member of the pair should:

b explain how we could reduce the amount of electricity we use at home.

Burning problems

1 Circle the correct answer. The word 'pollutant' means:

    a   a type of South American parrot

    b   a chemical made by human activity that damages the environment

    c   a chemical that makes an acid when it dissolves in water

    d   a chemical that kills plants

    e   a chemical that is used to make petrol

2 Match the pollutants released by burning with the problems they cause.

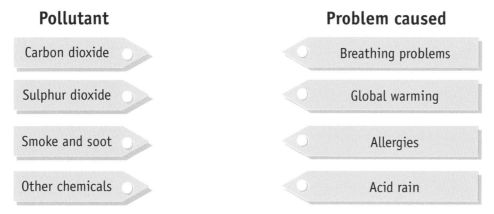

Pollutant	Problem caused
Carbon dioxide	Breathing problems
Sulphur dioxide	Global warming
Smoke and soot	Allergies
Other chemicals	Acid rain

3 **a** Circle the correct answer. What is the main source of air pollution in a large city like London or Tokyo?

    motor vehicles   drains   green plants   electricity substations   fast food restaurants

  b Suggest **two** ways to reduce pollution from motor vehicles.

    1 _____

    _____

    2 _____

    _____

4 The congestion charge in London is a tax on people driving their cars into the city centre.

Working in pairs, one member of the pair should:

a explain how the congestion charge affects pollution in the city centre.

The other member of the pair should:

b describe the problems caused by burning lots of fossil fuels.

Renewable energy resources

1 Sort these energy resources into the correct columns in the table below.

> oil   coal   solar   tidal   nuclear   bio-fuel

Renewable	Non-renewable

2 Give **one** advantage and **one** disadvantage of renewable and non-renewable energy resources.

Energy resources	Advantage	Disadvantage
Renewable		
Non-renewable		

3 What supplies the energy for each of these devices?

Device	Energy supplied by...
A wind-up torch	
An electricity-generating windmill	
A bicycle	
A solar-powered door bell	
A water mill for grinding corn	

4 The government wants to build a large wind farm a few miles from your home.

Working in pairs, one member of the pair should:

a explain what you feel about this development.

The other member of the pair should:

b explain how renewable energy resources can cause environmental problems.

What about nuclear power?

1 Circle the correct answer. The fuel used in nuclear power stations contains:

> kryptonite   carbon   uranium   einsteinium   generatium

2 Mark the following statements TRUE or FALSE.

a Nuclear power stations produce radioactive waste.

b Uranium reserves will last forever.

c Nuclear power stations produce very little carbon dioxide while they are working.

d Nuclear power stations are much more expensive to build than oil-fired power stations.

3 The following passage provides information about nuclear power. Use the words in the box to fill in the gaps and complete the text.

Nuclear power uses heat from nuclear reactions to .... water to make steam. This steam turns giant turbines. The turbines turn generators to make electricity. Nuclear .... stations do not produce much carbon .... when they are working. However, building and dismantling these power stations needs a lot of energy and this comes from burning .... fuels. Wastes made by nuclear power stations have to be stored for hundreds of thousands of years before they are................. .

> power   safe   fossil   dioxide   boil

4 Working in pairs, one member of the pair should:

a explain why we need to look at nuclear power as a way to generate electricity.

The other member of the pair should:

b describe some of the dangers of nuclear power.

What is sound?

1 Write a sentence to explain what the word 'vibration' means.

2 Match the instruments with the way they make a sound.

Instrument	Sound is made by...
Drum	scraping two things across each other
Trumpet	plucking a taut string
Violin	hitting something
Guitar	blowing down a tube

3 Use the words in the box below to fill the gaps in this passage.

Sounds are .... in the air. These vibrations can be made by a vibrating surface in a drum or a vibrating string on a.............. . Wind instruments like the flute make a .... of air in a tube vibrate. How quickly the air particles vibrate controls the .... of the note. More vibrations per second gives a higher pitched sound. The distance the particles vibrate controls the .... of the sound – the bigger the distance, the louder the sound.

vibrations	guitar	column	pitch	loudness

4 Working in pairs, one member of the pair should:

a pick any musical instrument and explain how it makes a sound.

The other member of the pair should:

b explain how a guitarist makes the volume of a note louder.

Describing sound

1 **a** Sort these sounds into a list based on their pitch, starting with the lowest.

The sounds bats use to find their way around   1 _____

A note on a bass guitar   2 _____

A soprano in an opera   3 _____

A typical telephone ring   4 _____

b Sort these sounds into a list based on their volume, starting with the quietest.

A jet plane taking off   1 _____

Normal speech   2 _____

A rock concert   3 _____

A whisper   4 _____

A car horn   5 _____

2 An oscilloscope can display the shape of a sound on a screen. Label the wave below by drawing a line from the label to the relevant part of the diagram.

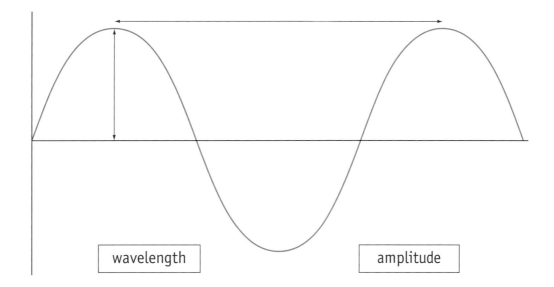

wavelength   amplitude

3 Working in pairs, one member of the pair should:

a explain what an oscilloscope can show about a sound.

The other member of the pair should:

b explain how the wavelength of a sound is linked to its frequency.

Speed of sound

1 Rank these into an order based on their speed, starting with the slowest.

Sound in metal	1	_____
A snail	2	_____
A beam of light	3	_____
A rocket taking off for the Moon	4	_____
Sound in air	5	_____

2 Explain what the word 'density' means.

3 a The speed of sound in the air is roughly 330 m/s. You are caught in a thunderstorm. At first you hear the thunder 3 seconds after you see the lightning. How far away is the storm?

b Five minutes later the lightning and thunder are separated by 1 second. How far away is the storm now?

c Is the storm getter closer or moving further away?

4 A student is measuring the distance to a large cliff. He makes a sound and the echo is heard 2 seconds later. How far away is the cliff?

5 Working in pairs, one member of the pair should:

a explain why North American Indians used to put their ears to the ground to hear the sound of buffalo stampeding many miles away.

The other member of the pair should:

b explain why the sound of an underground explosion gets to the other side of the planet even if it cannot be heard in the air.

Sound waves

1 Match these scientific words to their correct meanings.

Scientific word

Rarefraction

Dissipates

Transverse wave

Longitudinal wave

Compression

Meaning

Moving closer together

Moving further apart

A wave that moves particles closer together and further apart in line with its direction

A wave that moves particles side to side along its direction

To spread out

2 A slinky spring can be used to model a wave passing through a substance.

a Add labels to the diagram below.

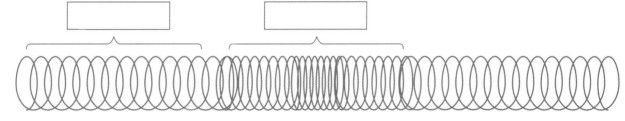

b Add an arrow to show which way the wave is moving for each diagram.

3 **a** Explain how a loudspeaker makes sounds in the air by moving a small cone of cardboard or plastic.

_____

b What sort of note is made when the cone moves very quickly but over short distances?

_____

c What sort of sound is made when the cone moves very slowly but over larger distances?

_____

4 Working in pairs, one member of the pair should:

a explain why the particles in a substance have not changed their position after a sound wave has passed.

The other member of the pair should:

b explain how the energy passes from particle to particle as a sound wave passes through a substance.

Sounds in solids, liquids and gases

1 Circle the correct answer. Which **one** of the following things CANNOT carry sound?

| a vacuum | metal | water | hydrogen gas | sound insulation |

2 You can make a toy telephone by linking two yoghurt pots together with string. When you speak into one pot the person at the other end can hear your voice if they hold their pot to their ear.

a How does the sound get to the person's ear?

_____

b Will the sound travel better if the string is pulled tight or left slack? Explain your answer.

_____

_____

3 Write a sentence to explain the word 'vibration'.

4 The following passage provides information about how sound travels. Use the words in the box to fill in the gaps and complete the text.

The .... in gases are quite far apart. They move easily but the energy in the sound wave spreads out very quickly in every direction. In a .... the particles are closer together. The .... pass easily between particles so the sound travels even more quickly. In a solid the particles are close together and held more tightly in place. It is more difficult to move them but because they are so close together even a small .... in one particle can affect the one next to it. For this reason the sound passes very quickly and can travel .... than in a liquid or gas.

| vibrations | movement | liquid | particles | further |

5 Working in pairs, one member of the pair should:

a explain why you cannot hear anything in space.

The other member of the pair should:

b explain why solid soundproofing materials for recording studios have lots of air spaces in them.

Ultrasonic sounds

1 Circle the correct answer. An ultrasonic sound is one that is:

    a   too low-pitched for humans to hear

    b   too high-pitched for humans to hear

    c   too quiet for humans to hear

    d   made by an ultraspeaker

    e   faster than normal sounds

2 Mark the following statements TRUE or FALSE.

    A   Human beings cannot hear sounds above 20 000 Hz.

    B   Bats and dogs can hear sounds above 20 000 Hz.

    C   Sounds with frequencies above 1 000 000 Hz are called ultrasonic.

    D   A piano produces ultrasonic sounds at the top end of the keyboard.

    E   Small children can hear ultrasonic sounds.

3 The following passage provides information about ultrasonic sound. Use the words in the box to fill in the gaps and complete the text.

Sound can make things............... . A loud bass note at a concert can make your body tingle! .... sounds are good at making small particles vibrate very quickly. This is used to clean bits of dirt from the .... of things like machinery or even human teeth. Doctors can also focus bursts of ultrasound on kidney................. . These stones are very painful but if they are made to vibrate by ultrasound they split up and the small .... pass out of the body with the urine.

> stones   vibrate   surface   ultrasonic   pieces

4 Working in pairs, one member of the pair should:

a give **three** uses of ultrasound.

The other member of the pair should:

b explain why ultrasound is useful for destroying structures inside the body.

The ear and hearing

1 Why should you never try to clean wax out of your ear by poking it with a sharp stick?

_____

_____

2 Draw a line between the labels and the correct structures in the ear.

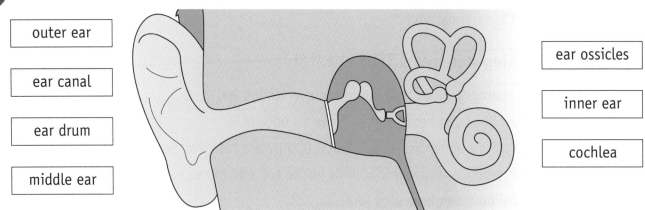

outer ear

ear canal

ear drum

middle ear

ear ossicles

inner ear

cochlea

3 Sort the following into the correct sequence to show how we hear a sound.

Sense cells in the cochlea converts vibrations into nerve impulses   1 _____

Outer ear collects sounds in the air around us   2 _____

Nerve impulses pass to the brain which interprets them as sounds   3 _____

Sounds pass along the ear canal and make the ear drum vibrate   4 _____

Eardrum passes vibrations onto the ear ossicles   5 _____

The ear ossicles pass vibrations into the cochlea   6 _____

4 The following passage provides information about how our ears help us to balance. Use the words in the box to fill in the gaps and complete the text.

The ears also help us to .... The semi-circular canals are three .... bent into half circles in the inner ear. They contain a liquid which swirls around when we move our head. Small paddle-like .... cells detect the movement of the liquid. They send .... to the .... and it interprets these to keep us balanced.

> balance   impulses   tubes   brain   sense

5 Working in pairs, one member of the pair should:

a explain what the ear ossicles do.

The other member of the pair should:

b explain why, when we have a cold and our middle ears are blocked with mucus, our hearing gets worse.

Damaging our hearing

1 Look at Tables 1 and 2 below then answer the questions that follow.

Table 1: What level of noise can damage your hearing?

Noise level in decibels (dB)	Can damage hearing after ...
140	Immediate damage – this is the threshold level for pain
120	7 minutes
100	2 hours a day
Less than 90	No damage

Table 2: Activity noise levels

Activity	Noise level (dB)
Going to a loud rock concert	110–130
Using a pneumatic drill	100
Going to a night club	110
Driving a speed boat	110
Watching jets taking off 0.5 km away	100
Using an electric shaver	85
Looking after a screaming child	90
Using a lawnmower	90

a Sound volume is measured in **dB**. What does dB stand for?

_____

b How long would you have to be exposed to sound of 120 dB for it to damage your hearing?

_____

c If a rock concert lasted 90 minutes would your hearing be damaged?

_____

d Why should people who use a pneumatic drill always wear ear defenders?

_____

2 Working in pairs, one member of the pair should:

a explain how you can protect your hearing against damage.

The other member of the pair should:

b explain how loud sounds can damage your hearing.

Heat and temperature

1 **a** Sort this list into temperature order, from coldest to warmest.

The snow on top of Everest	1	_____
Liquid air	2	_____
A supermarket freezer	3	_____
A nice cup of tea	4	_____
The flame on a gas cooker	5	_____
The boiling point of water	6	_____

b The temperature of one of the items in your list is −10 °C. Which item is it?

_____

c Circle the correct answer. The 'C' in '°C' stands for:

coldness   centigrade   Celsius   cool

2 Draw arrows to show which way heat flows in each of the pairs below. One has been done as an example.

Ice cubes in a cup of tea	Ice cubes	⟵	Tea
A metal rod in a Bunsen flame	Metal rod		Bunsen flame
An explorer on the ice in Iceland	Explorer		The ice
The surface of the road in the summer sun	Road surface		Summer sun
A beef burger on a barbecue	Beef burger		Barbecue coals

3 Circle the correct answer. What do we use to measure temperature?

thermal meter   theodolite   heatometer   thermometer

4 Working in pairs, one member of the pair should:

a explain **two** differences between heat and temperature.

The other member of the pair should:

b explain how to tell which way heat energy flows.

Getting warmer

1 Give **three** reasons why you might want to heat something up.

1 _____

2 _____

3 _____

2 List as many ways as possible to warm up a bowl of soup. Can you think of **five**?

1 _____

2 _____

3 _____

4 _____

5 _____

3 Describe what happens to each of the following things if they are heated with a Bunsen burner.

a A block of ice

_____

b An iron nail

_____

c A plastic cup

_____

d A bar of chocolate

_____

4 Working in pairs, one member of the pair should:

a explain how a pair of woolly gloves can keep your fingers warm even though the gloves do not have a heater in them.

The other member of the pair should:

b explain how a microwave oven heats up food.

Conduction

1 Sort the following things into the correct columns in the table below.

an iron bar   a gold bracelet   a steel nail

a woolly jumper   a plastic cup   a polar bear's fur coat

Good conductors	Poor conductors

2 **a** Suggest **two** uses for a good conductor of heat energy.

1 _____

2 _____

b Suggest **two** uses for a poor conductor of heat energy.

1 _____

2 _____

3 The following passage provides information about conduction. Use the words in the box to fill in the gaps and complete the text.

Solids tend to be .... conductors of heat energy. This is because the .... they contain are close together. When one starts to .... it makes the ones near it vibrate. In this way the heat .... passes through the solid. In liquids and gases the particles are further apart. The vibrations do not pass from particle to particle so easily. This is why liquids and gases are good ....

> good   insulators   vibrate   particles   energy

4 Working in pairs, one member of the pair should:

a explain why hot coffee in a tin mug cools more quickly than in a plastic mug.

The other member of the pair should:

b explain why ice cream is packed in plastic containers not metal dishes.

Convection

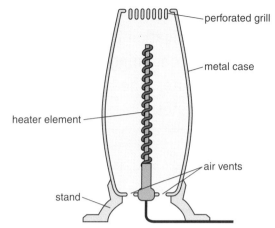

1 Add arrows to the diagram on the right to show how the air moves when the heater is switched on.

2 **a** Complete the grid, using the clues below to work out the answers.

1							T					
2							H					
3							E					
4							R					
5							M					
6							A					
7							L					
8							S					

CLUES

1 Heat moving through a solid by this process. (10 letters)
2 A form of energy that maker things get hotter. (4 letters)
3 Heat moving through a gas or liquid by moving parts of the gas or liquid. (10 letters)
4 Warm air .... above cold air. (5 letters)
5 Convection depends on the .... of hot liquids or gases. (8 letters)
6 A measure of how hot something is. (11 letters)
7 .... air sinks below warm air. (4 letters)
8 As a hot iron loses heat by convection its temperature .... (5 letters)

b Now write your own clue for the word 'thermals'.

_____

_____

3 Working in pairs, one member of the pair should:

a explain why a hot air balloon rises when the burner is switched on.

The other member of the pair should:

b explain why convection cannot happen in a solid.

Radiation

1 An investigation looked at how easily surfaces absorb radiation. Different coloured metal beakers containing water were placed in position and then a heat lamp switched on for five minutes. The temperature of the water was taken at the beginning and end of the five minutes.

Beaker colour	Temperature at start in °C	Temperature at end in °C	Change in temperature in °C
White	15	18	
Silver	15	19	
Black	15	26	

   a Complete the table above by working out the change in temperature for each beaker.

   b Draw a graph or chart to show the temperature rise for each beaker.

The experiment was repeated but this time only the black beaker was used. The scientist looked at the effect of distance from the lamp on heating of the water.

Distance from lamp in cm	Temperature rise in °C
25	14
50	8
70	3

   c Using information from both experiments, write down two conclusions.

   1 _____

   2 _____

2 Circle the correct answer. Infrared radiation is:

   a radiation that makes X-ray machines work
   b one way that heat travels through empty space
   c light that looks red in colour
   d what gives Superman his special powers

3 Explain the difference between reflectors and absorbers.

Topic checklist

5 Magnetism

Level 3
I know **two** metals that can be made into magnets. page 39
I know that magnets have a North and South pole. page 40
I know that like poles repel and unlike poles attract. page 40
I know **two** uses for an electromagnet. page 43
I know that a power station makes electricity. page 46
I know **three** fuels a power station could use. page 46

Level 4
I know what a magnetic field is. page 40
I know how to magnetise an iron bar with an electric current and a coil of wire. page 43
I know the difference between an electromagnet and a permanent magnet. page 43
I know how an electric bell works. page 44
I know that a motor converts electricity into movement and a generator converts movement into electricity. page 45
I can list **three** types of pollution. page 47
I know the difference between renewable and non-renewable energy resources. page 48
I know that nuclear power stations use uranium as fuel. page 49

6 Sound and heat

Level 3
I know that sound is a wave. page 51, page 53
I know how to protect my ears in noisy areas. page 57
I know **three** good conductors of heat. page 60
I know **three** good heat insulators. page 60

Level 4
I know how the frequency of a sound affects its pitch. page 50
I know what ultrasonic sound is and what it can be used for. page 55
I know how heat passes through solids by conduction. page 60
I know how heat passes through gases and liquids by convection. page 54, page 61
I know that heat can also travel by radiation. page 62

Topic quiz

5 Magnetism

1 List **three** metals which can be made into magnets.
2 **a** Where are the poles in a magnet?
  b What are the poles called?
3 What is a magnetic field?
4 Give **one** difference between an electromagnet and a permanent magnet.
5 How is a powerful electromagnet used to sort scrap metal?
6 What happens to a magnet if you place it in a coil and pass alternating current (electricity that changes direction very rapidly) through the coil?
7 Give **three** ways to increase the strength of the magnetic field in a coil.
8 Explain how the Earth's magnetic field is produced.
9 What are domains and how do they help to explain magnetism?
10 What happens when you bring the north pole of a compass near:
  a a north pole on a magnet
  b a south pole on a magnet?
11 **a** Mark the statements below TRUE or FALSE.
  b Rewrite the false statements to make them correct.
  • The magnetic field is strongest near the poles of a magnet.
  • Iron filings arrange themselves along the lines of magnetic force in a magnetic field.
  • The Earth's core cannot be a permanent magnet because it is too hot.
  • An electric bell contains an electromagnet which can be switched on and off very quickly.
  • Stronger electric currents produce more powerful electromagnets than weaker currents.
  • Aluminium is a magnetic material.
  • Electromagnets are always weaker than permanent magnets.
  • Generators convert electricity into movement.
  • Magnetic fields cannot pass through paper.

6 Sound and heat

1 What does the pitch of a sound measure?
2 What is the distance from the middle of a wave to the top called?
3 Which travels faster: sound or light?
4 What happens to air particles as a sound wave passes through them?
5 Draw a labelled diagram of the human ear.
6 What **two** things affect the damage a sound does to your ears?
7 Where might you need to use ear defenders?
8 Explain how sounds travel through solids.
9 What makes the sound in a piano?
10 Which is colder: ice at 0°C or water at 0°C? (Be careful!)
11 **a** What is conduction of heat?
  b What do we call something that cannot conduct heat?
12 **a** Mark the statements below TRUE or FALSE.
  b Rewrite the false statements to make them correct.
  • Sound cannot travel through the vacuum of space.
  • Ultrasonic sounds are too high pitched to be heard by humans.
  • Frequency is measured in Hertz.
  • Sound is a form of energy.
  • Sound travels at roughly 330m/sec.
  • The frequency of a sound controls its loudness.
  • Monocles are small bones in the human ear.
  • You can improve your hearing by eating lots of carrots.
  • Sound travels faster in gases than in solids.
  • Sound waves are transverse waves.
  • In radiation hot particles move to carry the heat energy.
  • Some materials get colder if you add heat energy to them.

Design a predator

1 Circle the correct answer. A predator is:

    A an animal that hunts and eats other animals

    B an animal that eats plants

    C an animal that is eaten by another animal

    D a robot

2 Match the features of the animal to the way it helps it to survive.

Feature	Helps it ...
a leopard's ability to run very fast	to stop its prey slipping out of its mouth
an owl has large eyes to see in the dark	to kill its prey
a rattlesnake produces poison	to catch prey
a shark has backward facing teeth	to see prey in dark environments

3 Use the words in the box below to fill the gaps in this passage.

A .... like a lion needs to be able to catch and kill its.............. The lion is .... to creep through the bush without its prey noticing. Strong jaws can kill the prey quickly and the sharp .... can cut into its flesh to remove all the meat from the body. The lion's prey has other .... to avoid being eaten.

predator	prey	camouflaged	teeth	adaptations

4 Working in pairs, one member of the pair should:

a explain why a predator that kills all of the prey in an area will eventually die itself.

The other member of the pair should:

b suggest **two** ways in which a tiger is adapted as a predator.

Where has the ox gone?

1 Suggest **three** ways in which energy in an animal is wasted when it is eaten by a predator.

1 _____

2 _____

3 _____

2 Write a sentence to explain the meaning of the word 'scavenger'.

_____

_____

3 Use the words in the box below to fill the gaps in this passage.

All living things need a supply of.............. Plants get this from the sun by photosynthesis. All animals get it from their .... - either plants or other animals. Because energy is always .... when an animal eats, the total amount of energy available goes down as there are more links in the food chain. This is why there are always .... lions in an area than...............

| energy | food | wasted | fewer | zebras |

4 Working in pairs, one member of the pair should:

a explain what a pyramid of numbers shows.

The other member of the pair should:

b suggest what a dung beetle eats.

Population models

1 List **six** factors that affect the size of the population of an animal in an area. Add them to the correct column in the table below.

Physical factors	Catastrophes	Biological factors

2 Circle the correct answer. A scientific model is something that:

    A behaves in the same way as the thing it is modelling

    B is made of plastic and clay

    C is always coloured red

    D has to run in a computer

    E is available in a model shop.

3 Use the words in the box below to fill the gaps in this passage.

Scientists use .... to investigate the way a population changes. Complex models use .... to predict what will happen according to certain rules. One advantage of computer models is that they can be run much more ....than the thing they are modelling. .... changes in humans are modelled in large computers by scientists. They can even run them forward to .... the human population in 20 or 50 years time.

>   models   computers   quickly   population   predict

4 Working in pairs, one member of the pair should:

a explain how a model can be used to protect fish stocks.

The other member of the pair should:

b explain the meaning of the word simulation.

Recycling by rotters

1 Sort this list into two groups: things that are decayed by living organisms and those that are not.

diamond   leaf litter   fish bones   tin cans   horse manure   car tyres

Living organisms help these things to decay	Living organisms cannot make these things decay

2 Give **two** advantages of using kitchen waste to make compost.

1 _____

2 _____

3 Use the words in the box below to fill the gaps in this passage.

Living things .... when they die. This decay is caused by a range of different organisms. Some can make wood decay. You may have seen .... growing on fallen logs. The mushrooms release chemicals which .... parts of the wood. Other .... then take over and break the wood down even further. Eventually the wood is converted to water, carbon .... and minerals in the soil.

decay   mushrooms   dissolve   microbes   dioxide

4 Working in pairs, one member of the pair should:

a explain what the word 'biodegradable' means.

The other member of the pair should:

b explain why tiny particles of plastic can be found all over the world - even in the Antarctic oceans!

Populations

1 Write a sentence to explain the meaning of the word 'population'.

2 **a** Suggest **two** things that could cause an increase in the population of rats in a town.

1 _____

2 _____

b Suggest **two** things that might cause a fall in the rat population in a town.

1 _____

2 _____

3 Use the words in the box below to fill the gaps in this passage.

Animals produce many more .... than they need just to replace themselves. However, their population remains pretty .... over many years. This means that many of the young do not survive to become adults. Only the .... or the luckiest survive. If there is a massive increase in .... of a species this can actually damage their environment and the large population will .... back to low numbers while the environment recovers.

| young | stable | fittest | population | crash |

4 Working in pairs, one member of the pair should:

a explain why a rise in predators in an area will lead to a fall in prey population.

The other member of the pair should:

b explain why a fall in the prey population in an area will lead to a decrease in the predator population.

Biological control

1 Name a pest that might eat each of these plants.

Plant	Pest
Lettuce	
Cabbage	
Roses	

2 **a** Suggest **one** advantage to a vegetable gardener of using a pesticide.

b Suggest **one** disadvantage to a vegetable gardener of using a pesticide.

3 Use the words in the box below to fill the gaps in this passage.

.... control uses living organisms to kill.............. The main advantage of this system is that no .... pesticides are needed. And if the number of pests goes up the population of organisms that feed on them also .... Ladybirds act as biological control organisms for greenfly on roses and whitefly in tomato greenhouses. The ladybirds do not .... the crops and help to keep the pests in check.

biological	pests	poisonous	rise	damage

4 Working in pairs, one member of the pair should:

a explain why a pesticide can often kill pests in a crop more quickly than a biological control system.

The other member of the pair should:

b explain why some pests cannot be controlled by biological control methods.

Day and night

1 Where does the light and heat on Earth come from?

2 Mark the statements below TRUE or FALSE.

    A   The Earth takes 24 hours to spin once on its axis.

    B   Half of the Earth is always pointing towards the Sun.

    C   The Earth moves round the Sun roughly every 365 days.

    D   The Sun moves around the Earth going from east to west across the sky.

    E   All planets in the Solar System have the same day length as the Earth.

3 Use the words in the box below to fill the gaps in this passage.

The Earth completes an .... of the Sun every 365¼ days. The extra six hours isn't much in a year but over a .... the extra time would be 25 days. This means Christmas would not arrive until January 19th! To stop this happening every .... years an extra day is added to February. These years are called .... years and help to keep our calendars in sync with the movement of the..............

> orbit   century   four   leap   Earth

4 Working in pairs, one member of the pair should:

a give **two** pieces of evidence that show that the Earth is a sphere.

The other member of the pair should:

b explain why we do not fly off the Earth even though it is constantly spinning.

The seasons

1 Match the following times with the events.

Times	Events
365.25 days	Time for the Earth to spin once on its axis
12 hours	Time for the Earth to complete one orbit of the Sun
8 hours	Length of the day at the spring equinox
24 hours	Length of the longest day of the year in the UK
16 hours 30 minutes	Length of the day on December 21st in the UK

2 a Complete the grid, using the clues below to work out the answers.

1						S				
2						E				
3						A				
4						S				
5						O				
6						N				
7						S				

CLUES

1 What nationality was Nicolaus Copernicus? (6 letters)
2 The Earth is a giant .... (6 letters)
3 The force attracting two masses together. (7 letters)
4 The winter .... is the shortest day of the year. (8 letters)
5 The imaginary line separating the northern and southern hemispheres. (7 letters)
6 The season in the UK when the northern hemisphere tilts away from the Sun. (6 letters)
7 The season in the UK when the northern hemisphere tilts towards the Sun. (6 letters)

b Now write your own clue for the word 'seasons'.

_____

_____

3 Working in pairs, one member of the pair should:

a explain how the tilt in the Earth's axis produces the different seasons.

The other member of the pair should:

b explain what a satellite is.

The Moon

1 Mark the following statements TRUE or FALSE.

  a   The Moon is Earth's only natural satellite.

  b   The Moon takes 28 days to orbit the Earth.

  c   The Moon's shape changes as it orbits the Earth.

  d   The Moon is about 1500 km from the Earth.

  e   Eclipses of the Moon only happen during the summer.

2 On a separate piece of paper draw the view **from the Earth** for each of the Moon positions in the diagram below.

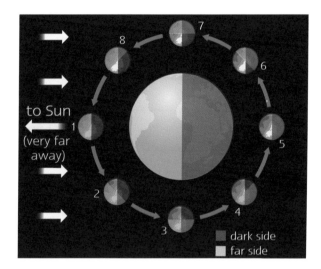

3 The following passage provides information about the Moon. Use the words in the box to fill in the gaps and complete the text.

The Moon .... the Earth every 28 days and sometimes it passes between the Earth and the......... . If it lines up exactly it can block the light from the Sun coming towards the Earth. This is called a solar.............. . Of course, there are times when the Moon is on the .... side of the Earth to the Sun. In this case the Earth blocks the sunlight to the Moon. This is called a .... eclipse.

| eclipse | lunar | Sun | orbits | other |

4 Working in pairs, one member of the pair should:

  a explain how we can see the Moon even though it produces no light like the Sun.

The other member of the pair should:

  b explain what a phase of the Moon is.

The Solar System

1 Sort these planets into the correct order starting with the one nearest the Sun.

Jupiter	1	_____
Venus	2	_____
Uranus	3	_____
Mars	4	_____
Earth	5	_____
Saturn	6	_____
Mercury	7	_____
Neptune	8	_____

2 Match these planets to their descriptions.

Planet	Description
Saturn	Sometimes called the Red Planet, humans have landed a robot spaceship there
Mercury	The largest planet in the Solar System
Jupiter	Rings of debris spin around the middle of this planet
Mars	So far away from the Sun it is covered in frozen gases. So small that some people say it may not even be a planet!

3 The following passage provides information about the Solar System. Use the words in the box to fill in the gaps and complete the text.

The Solar .... consists of one star and .... planets. The star, which we call the Sun, is by far the biggest object in the Solar System. Its diameter is 1000 times Earth's. .... reactions generate huge amounts of energy and we see these as sunlight. .... are smaller and do not give out their own light. The distances between the planets are much bigger than the distances across the Sun. So the Solar System is largely ....

System	empty	planets	eight	nuclear

4 Working in pairs, one member of the pair should:

a explain how telescopes have helped us to understand our Solar System.

The other member of the pair should:

b explain what conditions would be like on Mercury and Venus.

Gravity in space

1 Circle the correct answer. Gravity is the force that:

    a   pushes masses apart

    b   pulls magnets together

    c   pulls two masses together

    d   pushes like electric charges apart

    e   pulls unlike electric charges together

2 Circle the correct answer. The first person to understand gravity was:

Isaac Newton   Isaac Walton   Charles Darwin   John Dalton   Archimedes

3 Which **two** of the following affect the strength of gravity between two objects? Circle your answers.

    a   What they are made from

    b   Their mass

    c   The speed they are moving

    d   Their electrical charge

    e   The distance apart

4 The following passage provides information about gravity. Use the words in the box to fill in the gaps and complete the text.

.... is the force that holds the Universe together. It acts between any .... and always pulls them together. You are .... towards the Earth because of the force of gravity. You also pull the Earth towards you. But your mass is so small compared with the planet that you move much more than the planet! That's why you fall towards it. The force of gravity depends on the masses of the two objects and the .... between them. The larger the masses and the shorter the distance the .... the force.

distance   gravity   pulled   bigger   masses

5 Working in pairs, one member of the pair should:

a explain how the Sun's gravity stops the Earth flying into space.

The other member of the pair should:

b explain why rockets need so much fuel to get into space.

Gravity and weight

1 What units is force measured in? Circle your answer.

> grams   newtons   pounds   gravitons   warp factors

2 Circle the correct answer. The mass of an elephant is:

a the amount of material it is made from

b its weight

c the height times the width

d the weight of leaves it eats every day

e the force that pulls it towards the Earth

3 a Complete the grid, using the clues below to work out the answers.

1				G			
2				R			
3				A			
4				V			
5				I			
6				T			
7				Y			

CLUES

1 A unit used to measure mass. (4 letters)

2 This is what gravity does to two masses. (7 letters)

3 The amount of substance in a body. (4 letters)

4 Gravity will make you do this if you jump out of a plane. (4 letters)

5 The force of gravity acting on a mass. (6 letters)

6 The unit of force. (6 letters)

7 Satellites do this around the Earth. (3 letters)

b Now write your own clue for the word 'gravity'.

_____

_____

4 Working in pairs, one member of the pair should:

a explain the difference between weight and mass.

The other member of the pair should:

b explain why you weigh less on the Moon even though your mass has not changed.

Satellites

1 List **three** things that we use satellites for.

1 _____

2 _____

3 _____

2 Explain why you need at least **two** satellites to make a mobile phone call to the other side of the planet.

_____

3 What is the Earth's only natural satellite?

_____

4 The following passage provides information about satellites. Use the words in the box to fill in the gaps and complete the text.

The very first satellite put into space was .... 1 in 1957. Nowadays there are thousands of satellites in .... around the Earth. Some change their positions. Others, called geostationary satellites, are always above the same .... on the planet's surface. They move in step with the planet. These geostationary satellites are used for .... networks. Putting a satellite into orbit is not cheap! It needs a very large rocket to push it up against Earth's gravitational.................

Sputnik   orbit   spot   communications   pull

5 Working in pairs, one member of the pair should:

a explain why photographs of the Earth from satellites might be useful.

The other member of the pair should:

b explain why satellites need large rockets to get into space.

Space travel

1 Give **two** reasons why people might want to explore space.

1 _____

2 _____

2 Circle the correct answer. Escape velocity is the speed:

a   needed to escape the pull of Earth's gravity

b   an object falls from a plane in flight

c   people run away from falling objects

d   exhaust comes out of a rocket motor

e   that a speeding motorist has to go to get away from a police motorcyclist

3 Escape velocity is lower on the Moon than on Earth. Explain why.

_____

_____

4 Space rockets need large amounts of fuel. Suggest **three** things they need fuel to do.

1 _____

2 _____

3 _____

5 The following passage provides information about space travel. Use the words in the box to fill in the gaps and complete the text.

Escaping from Earth is not easy! .... pulls objects down towards the .... and the larger the object the greater the force. Rockets are very large because they need a lot of .... to power the engines to push against gravity. But more fuel means more weight! The Saturn V rocket that took humans to the Moon .... over 2 700 000 kg but the capsule that made the trip to the Moon was less than 100 000 kg. Most of the rocket was fuel. Once the rocket got into space it needed much less fuel because the force of gravity is so much................. .

> planet   lower   fuel   gravity   weighed

6 Eexplain why even a rocket as powerful as the Saturn V would take too long to get to the nearest star.

Exploring further

1 Give **two** ways we can find out what Mars is like.

1 _____

2 _____

2 Circle the correct answer. Modern space exploration uses robot probes rather than spaceships with people in them. Why?

    a   People cost too much money

    b   People are not as clever as robots

    c   Robot probes can be smaller and need fewer supplies

    d   No one wants to go into space

    e   Health and safety regulations do not allow people to travel fast enough to get into space

3 Put ticks to show which planets each of these passed near or landed on.

Probe	Mars	Jupiter	Saturn	Neptune	Uranus
Pioneer 10					
Voyager 1 and 2					
Pathfinder					

4 What is the name of the large telescope orbiting the Earth?

_____

5 Working in pairs, one member of the pair should:

a explain why a telescope above the Earth's atmosphere gives a clearer picture than one on the surface.

The other member of the pair should:

b explain what a probe actually landing on a planet can tell us that a telescope cannot.

Topic checklist

7 Life and death

Level 3

Level 4

8 Space

Level 3

Level 4

Topic quiz

7 Life and death

1 List **three** adaptations of zebras to avoid being eaten by lions.
2 Why do animals waste energy when they eat other animals?
3 What is a pyramid of numbers?
4 Give **two** physical factors that affect the population of an organism.
5 What does the word migration mean in animal populations?
6 Why do scientists use computer models for population studies?
7 Explain how you could decide if a plastic bag was biodegradable or not.
8 Why do compost bins need a supply of air?
9 What helps to keep animal populations stable even when they produce many more young than they need?
10 Give **two** advantages of biological control for pests.
11 a Mark the statements below TRUE or FALSE.
   b Rewrite the false statements to make them correct.
   • Camouflage helps animals to move around but not be seen by predators or prey.
   • Energy is wasted when an animal eats another animal.
   • An increase in food supply almost always leads to an increase in animal populations.
   • A food web shows the feeding relationships in an area.
   • If predators fall in number, the prey population tends to rise.
   • Only predators have adaptations, prey animals have none.
   • 99% of the energy in grass is wasted when it is eaten by a cow.
   • Leaf litter is broken down by cows and sheep.
   • Greenfly are good organisms to control ladybird populations.
   • Fungicides are used to kill weeds.

8 Space

1 a How many days are in a year?
   b How many months are in a year?
2 What is the Earth's only natural satellite called?
3 a How many planets are there in the Solar System?
   b How many stars are there in the Solar System?
4 What force pulls you towards the centre of the Earth?
5 a What is weight measured in?
   b Explain why you would weigh less on the Moon.
6 What is 'escape velocity'?
7 What was Voyager II?
8 Which is the smallest planet in the Solar System?
9 Which planet in the Solar System has rings around it?
10 Explain why the Moon seems to change shape over a month.
11 a Mark the statements below TRUE or FALSE.
   b Rewrite the false statements to make them correct.
   • Sputnik 1 was the first artificial satellite.
   • Satellites are used for communications and surveying the Earth.
   • Copernicus was a polish astronomer who suggested the Sun was at the centre of the Solar System.
   • An eclipse occurs when the Moon passes in front of the Sun.
   • Christmas day is warm in Australia but June can be cold and wet.
   • An orbit is a square path around the Earth.
   • Most of the weight of the Saturn V rocket was electronic computers.
   • Saturn is able to produce its own light.
   • The Earth is at the centre of the Sun and planets.
   • The seasons are caused by the daily spin of the Earth.

Glossary/Index

Glossary/Index